Color and Trace

Aa

Aa

Color and Trace

Bb

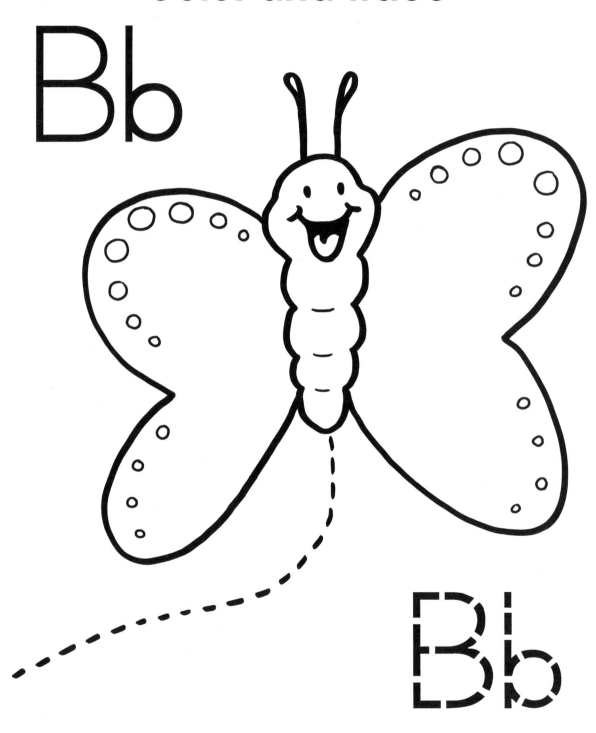

Bb

Brighter Vision Homework Helper

Color and Trace

C c

C c

Color and Trace

Dd

Dd

Color and Trace

Ee

Ee

Color and Trace

Ff

Ff

Color and Trace

Color and Trace

Hh

Hh

Color and Trace

I i

I i

Color and Trace

J j

J j

Color and Trace

K k

K k

Color and Trace

L l

L l

Color and Trace

Color and Trace

Nn

Nn

Color and Trace

Color and Trace

P p

The Joy of Mud

P p

Color and Trace

Qq

Qq

Color and Trace

Rr

Rr

Color and Trace

Color and Trace

T t

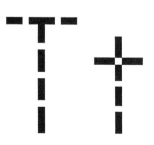

Color and Trace

Uu

Uu

Color and Trace

V v

I Love
You!

V v

Color and Trace

Ww

W W w

Color and Trace

Color and Trace

Y y

YARN

Y y

Color and Trace

Zz

Zz

Say the Alphabet

Aa Bb Cc

Dd Ee Ff Gg

Hh Ii Jj Kk

Ll Mm Nn Oo

Pp Qq Rr Ss

Tt Uu Vv Ww

Xx Yy Zz

Compare

Circle the letters that match
the letter on the sign.

(B) B

B

R H B

D

B B

P E

B

B A B

Look Carefully

Draw lines between the matching letters.

A	F	B	D
P	A	C	G
F	K	D	B
K	P	G	C

E	E	M	L
H	J	N	N
J	I	L	O
I	H	O	M

Twins

In each row, color the creatures that have the same letter.

Study the Letters

Draw lines between the matching letters.

Y	Z	R	P
V	Y	D	B
X	V	P	R
Z	X	B	D
Q	G	T	L
G	C	H	E
S	Q	E	H
C	S	L	T

Alike and Different

Color all of the monsters that have the same letter as the monster in this box.

Lowercase Letters

Draw lines between the matching letters.

m	r
n	u
r	m
u	n

g	c
c	e
e	g
q	q

f	j
i	t
t	i
j	f

a	d
p	a
b	p
d	b

Uppercase Letters

Connect the dots from A to Z.

Brighter Vision Homework Helper

Lowercase Letters

Connect the dots from a to z.

Matching Time!

Draw lines between the letters that have the same name.

A	n	E	f
H	a	L	t
N	m	F	e
M	h	T	l
B	d	R	i
D	g	P	k
G	q	K	r
Q	b	I	p

Don't Forget These Letters!

Trace each letter.
Say the name of the letter.

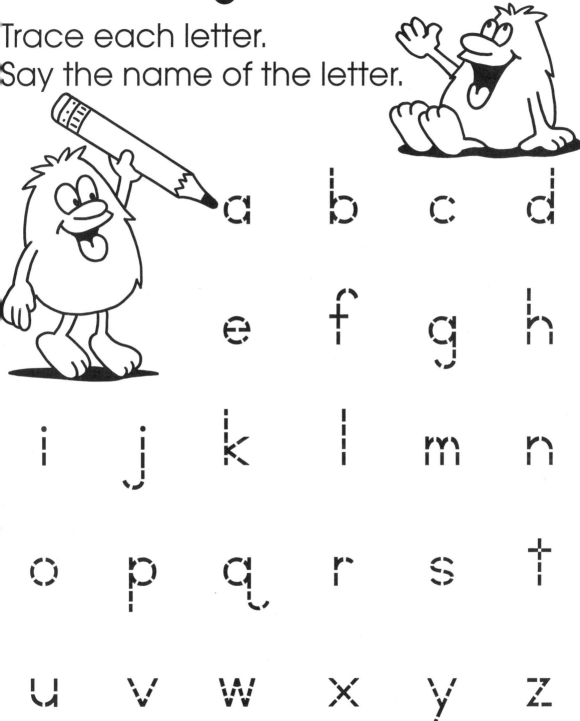

a   b   c   d

e   f   g   h

i   j   k   l   m   n

o   p   q   r   s   t

u   v   w   x   y   z

B Is for Butterfly

Color the pictures that begin with B.

S Is for Seal

Color the pictures that begin with S.

D Is for Dog

Color the pictures that begin with **D**.

M Is for Mouse

Color the pictures that begin with **M**.

P Is for Panda

Color the pictures that begin with **P**.

Brighter Vision Homework Helper

T Is for Tiger

Color the pictures that begin with **T**.

R Is for Rabbit

Color the pictures that begin with R.

K Is for Kangaroo

Color the pictures that begin with **K**.

 J Is for Jack-in-the-Box

Color the pictures that begin with J.

L Is for Lion

Color the pictures that begin with L.

L l

F Is for Fish

Color the pictures that begin with **F**.

Say the Word!

Circle the correct beginning sound.
Color the picture.

Ss   Bb   Ss   Bb

Ss   Bb   Ss   Bb

How Does It Start?

Circle the correct beginning sound.
Color the picture.

T t   M m

T t   M m

T t   M m

T t   M m

What Is the Sound?

Circle the correct beginning sound.
Color the picture.

Rr   Kk   Rr   Kk

Rr   Kk   Rr   Kk

One Alligator

Color the Pictures

1 bear

1 gorilla

1 frog

1 bee

Two Rabbits

Look for Twos

Color every animal that has a **2** on it.

Three Cats

3 3 3 3 3

Go, Go, Go!

Color every car that has a **3** on it.

Four Bats

Fun With Four

Color every space that has a **4** in it.

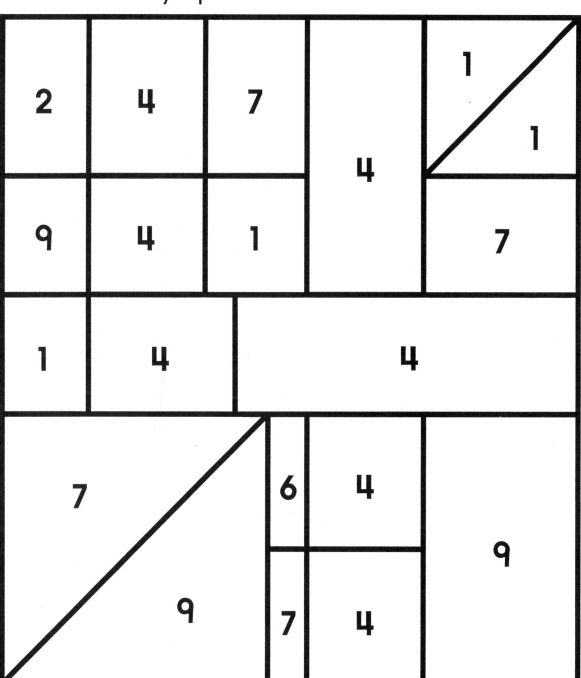

Five Butterflies

5

Looking for Fives

Color every animal that has a **5** on it.

Six Snakes

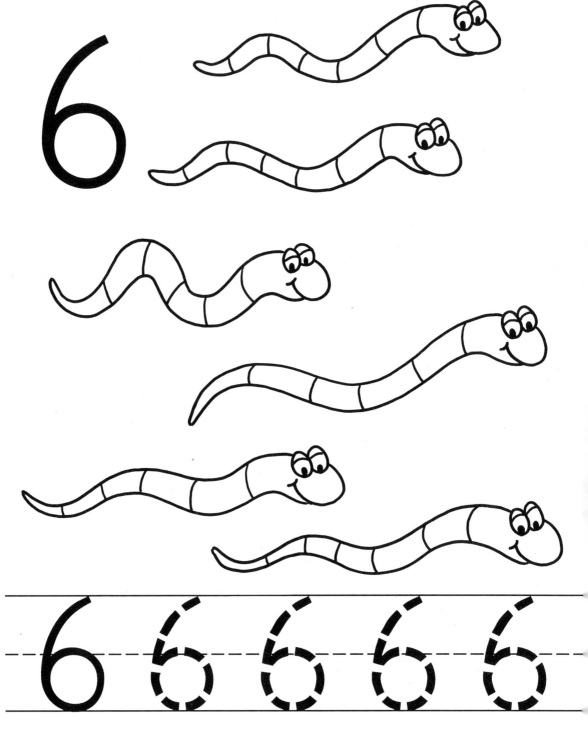

Searching for Six

Draw a circle around every 6 hidden in the picture.

Seven Caterpillars

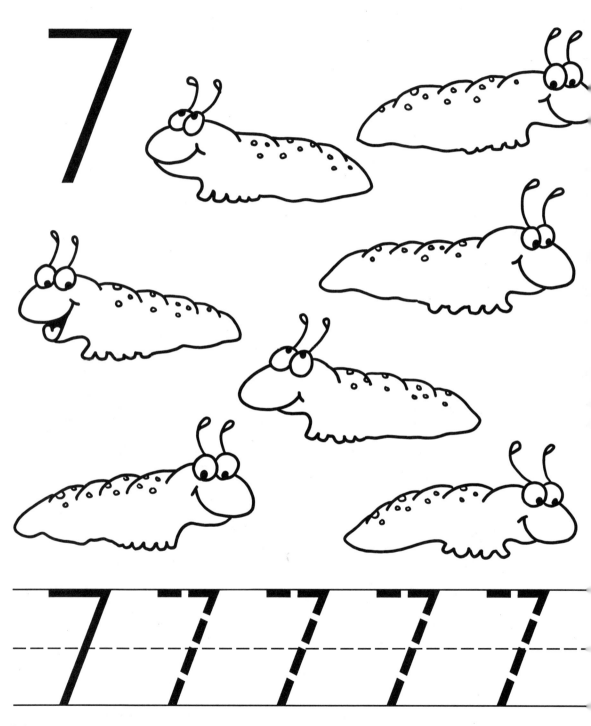

Counting to Seven

Color 7 balloons.

Eight Starfish

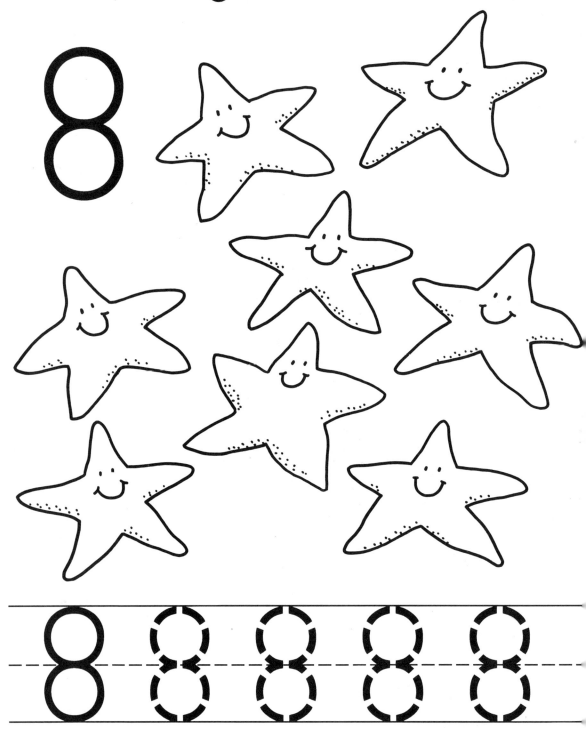

Eight Is Great!

Color every animal that has an **8** on it.

Nine Fish

Look Carefully

Circle all of the nines.

(9)	9	6	9	2
9	6	5	4	9
9	9	9	0	8
9	8	6	9	2
8	9	9	9	6

Ten Ladybugs

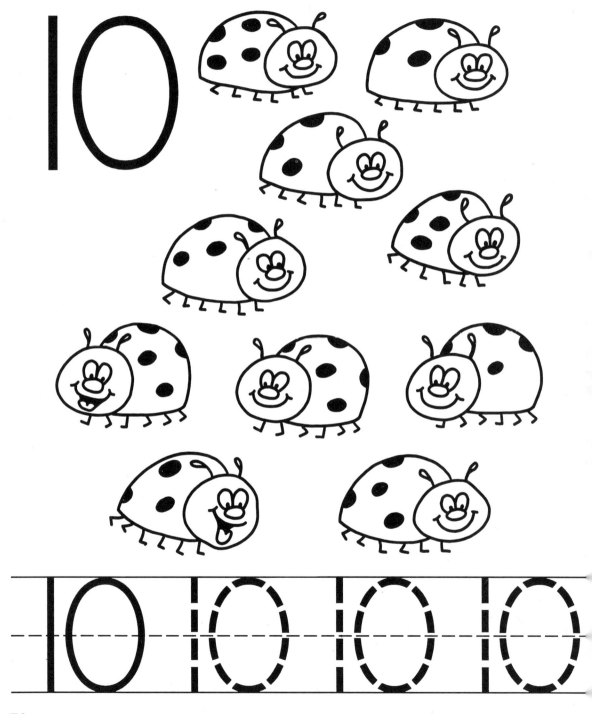

Looking for Tens

Color every animal that has a **10** on it.

Color 1.

Color 2.

Color 3.

Color 4.

Color 5.

Color 6.

Color 7.

Color 8.

Color 9.

Color 10.

Counting Time

Circle the correct number in each box.

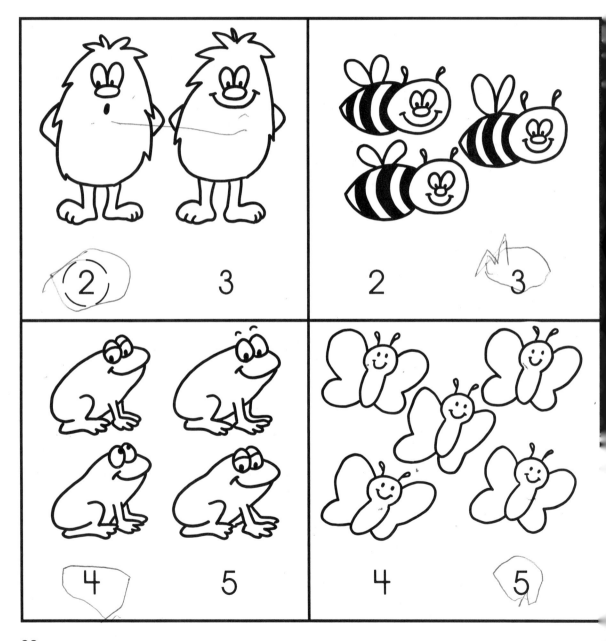

Count and Color

Circle the correct number in each box.

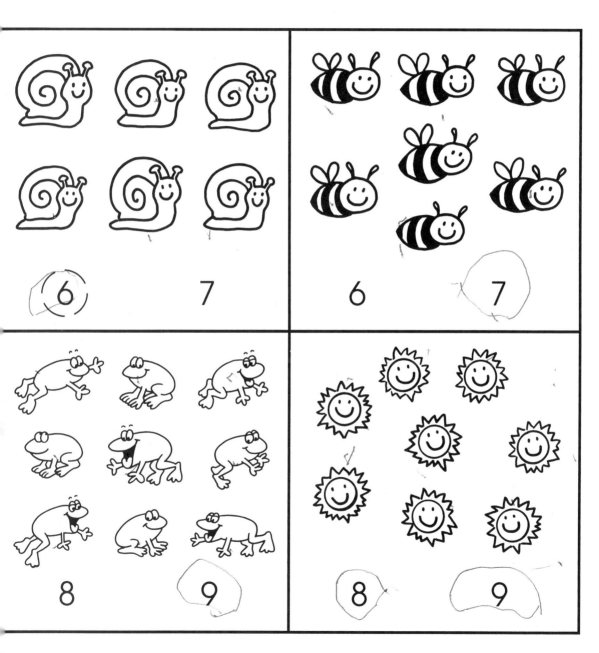

Dot-to-Dot

Connect the dots from 1 to 5.

Brighter Vision Homework Helper

Count First

Color 2.

Color 4.

Color 3.

Color 5.

Draw Spots

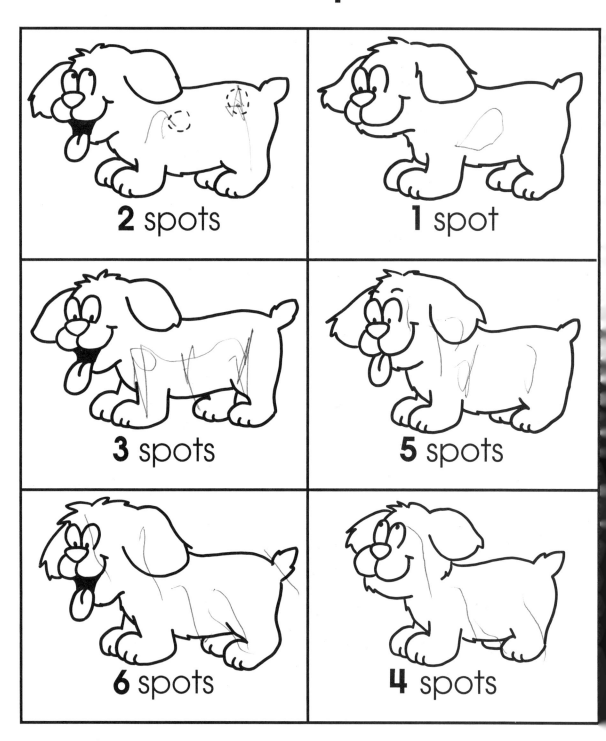

2 spots

1 spot

3 spots

5 spots

6 spots

4 spots

Count Before You Color

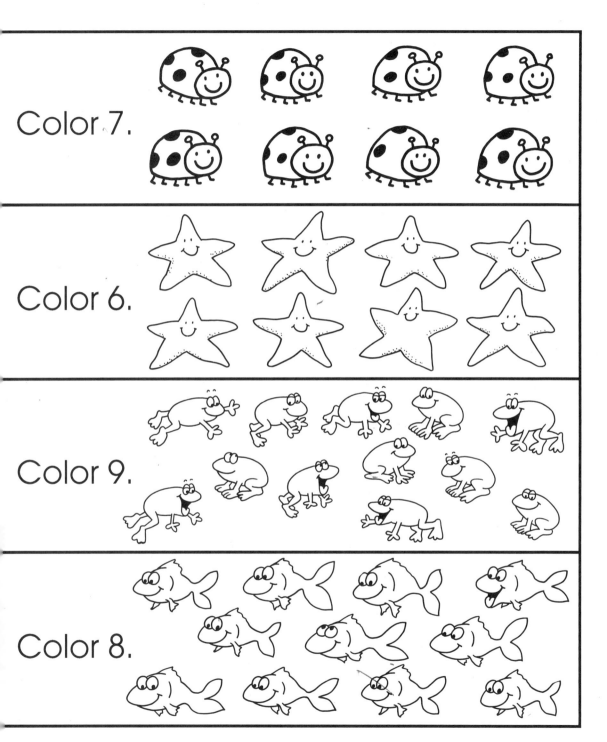

Color 7.

Color 6.

Color 9.

Color 8.

What Is It?

Connect the dots from 1 to 10.

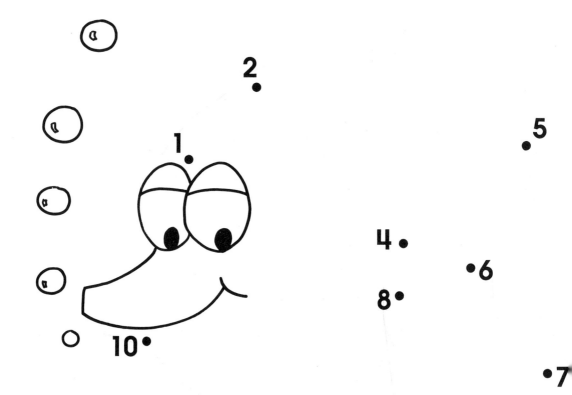

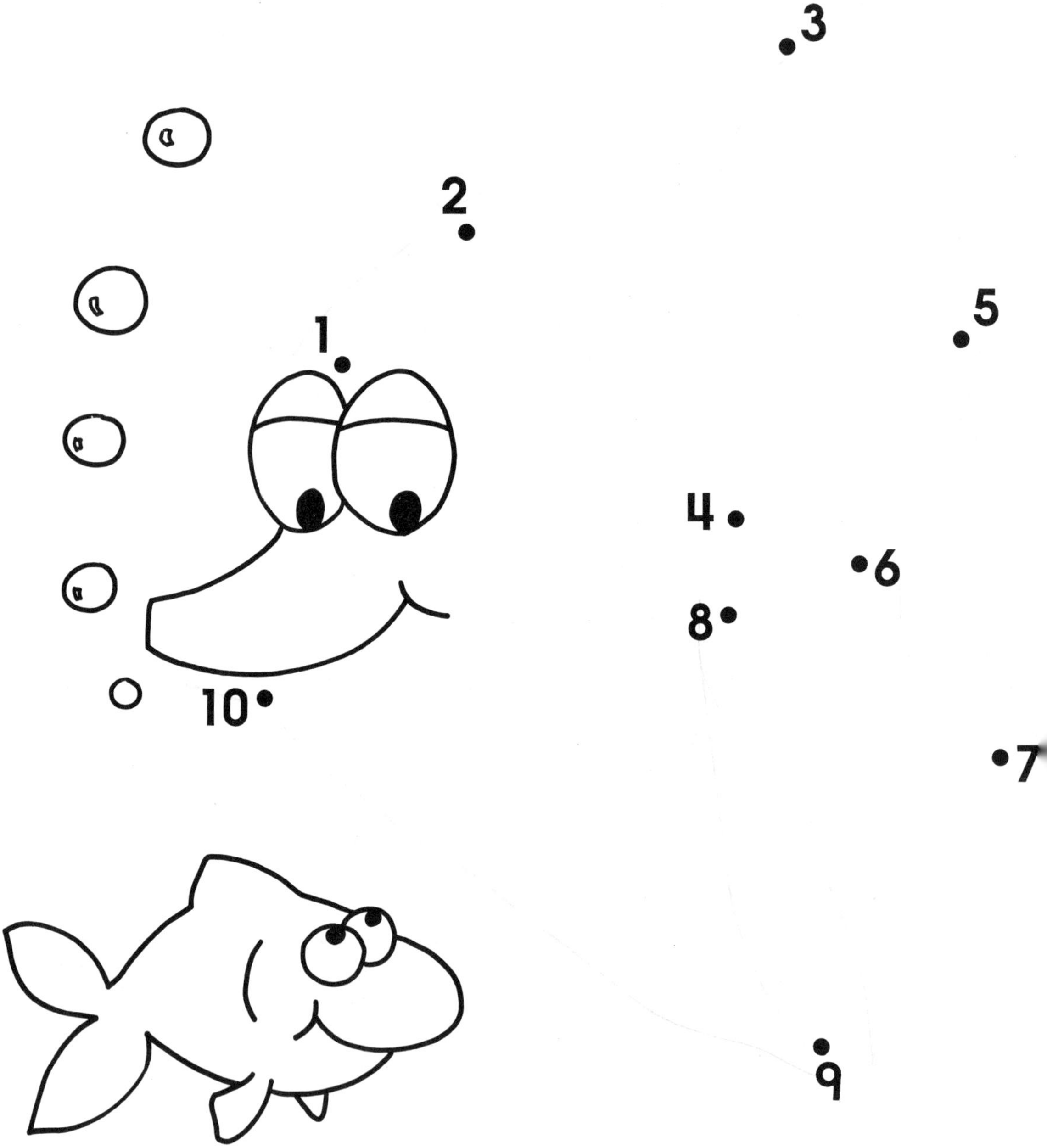

.3

2

.5

1

4 .

•6

8 •

10 •

•7

•9

Time to Write

Practice each number four times.

1 1	
2 2	
3 3	
4 4	
5 5	

More Numbers

Practice each number.

6   6

7   7

8   8

9   9

10   10

How Many?

Count the objects in each set.
Write the number on the line.

Dot-to-Dot

Connect the dots from 1 to 10.

Count Carefully

Count the objects in each set.
Write the number on the line.

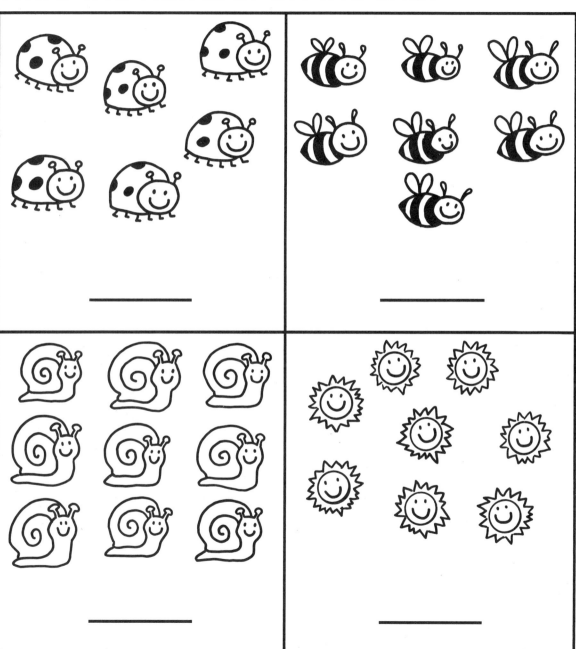

_____   _____

_____   _____

Which Has More?

In each row, circle the set that has more. Color the pictures.

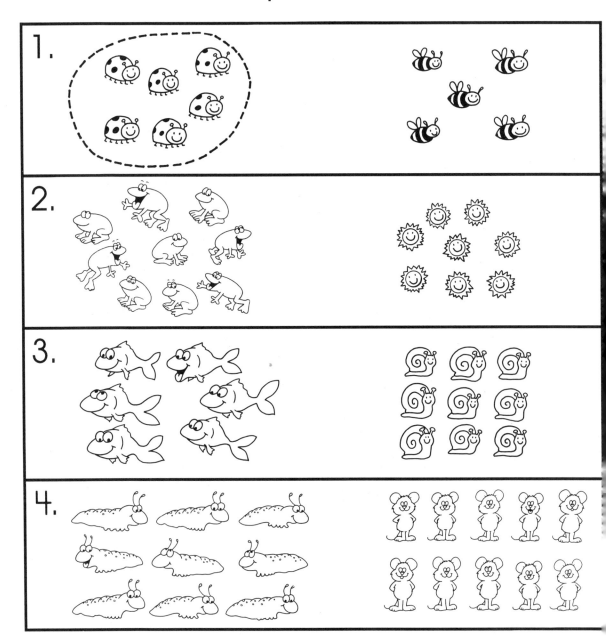

Which Has Fewer?

n each row, circle the set that has
ewer. Color the pictures.

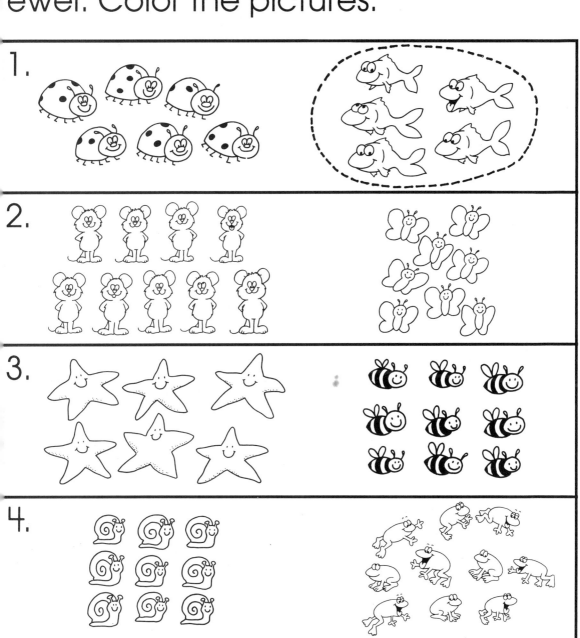

From Memory!

Write the numbers from 1 to 10.

Number Words

Read and trace.

1   one   one

2   two   two

3   three   three

4   four   four

5   five   five

Matching

Draw a line from each number to its number word.

1   two

2   one

3   five

4   four

5   three

Read and Color

Color five.

Color one.

Color four.

Color three.

Color two.

More Number Words

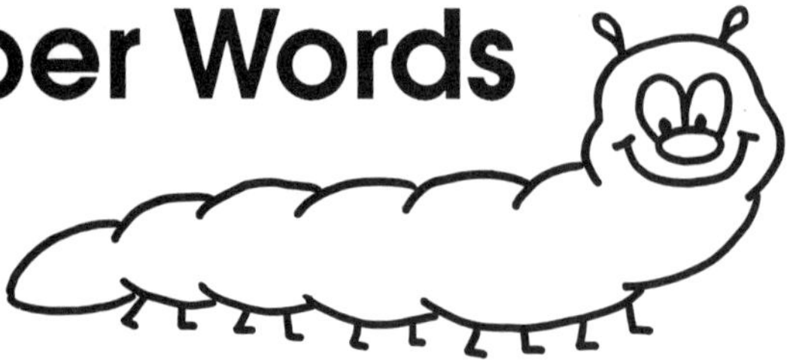

Read and trace.

6 six   six

7 seven seven

8 eight eight

9 nine   nine

10 ten   ten

More Matching

Draw a line from each number to its number word.

6

7

8

9

10

nine

six

eight

ten

seven

Read and Color

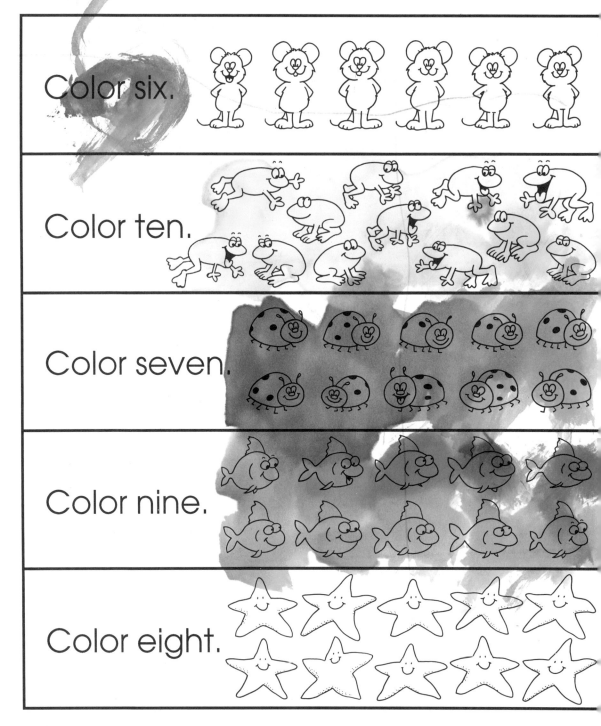

Color six.

Color ten.

Color seven.

Color nine.

Color eight.

Brighter Vision Homework Helpe

A Pretty Sight

Help Tyler get close to the butterfly.

Square

Color.

Trace.

square

Let's Make Squares

Trace. Color.

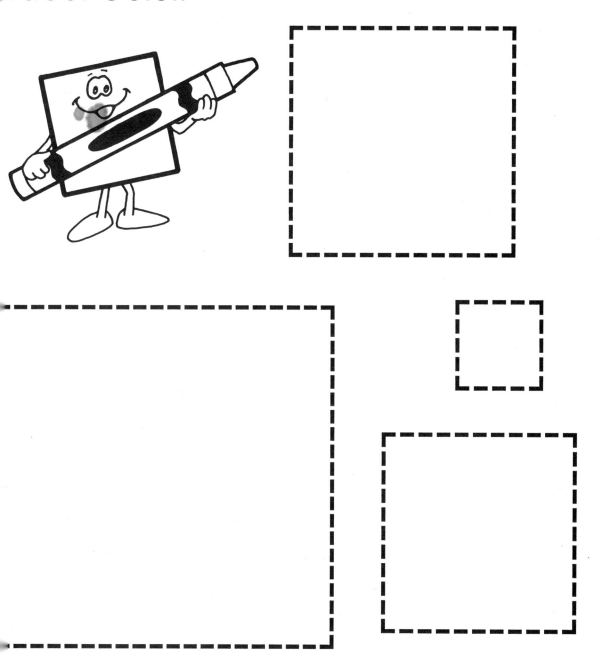

Small, Medium, and Large Squares

Match by size. Color.

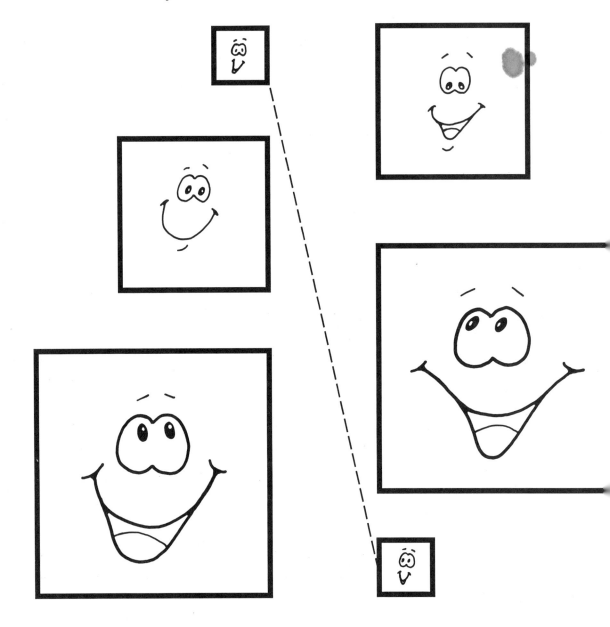

Which Are Squares?

Color the squares.

Find the Squares

Color only the squares.

I Can Draw Squares!

Trace.   Draw.

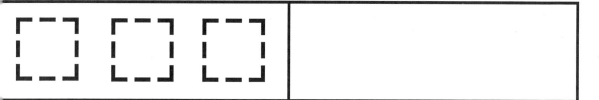

Draw a picture with squares in it.

Circle

Color.

Trace.

circle

Let's Make Circles

Trace. Color.

Small, Medium, and Large Circles

Match by size. Color.

162

Which Are Circles?

Color the circles.

Find the Circles

Color only the circles.

I Can Draw Circles!

Trace.   Draw.

Draw a picture with circles in it.

Triangle

Color.

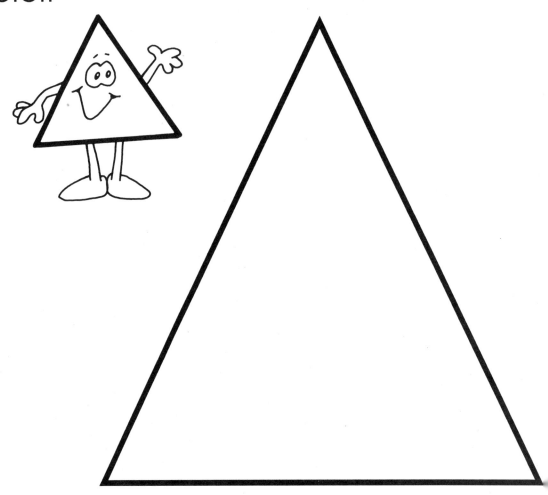

Trace.

triangle

Let's Make Triangles

Trace. Color.

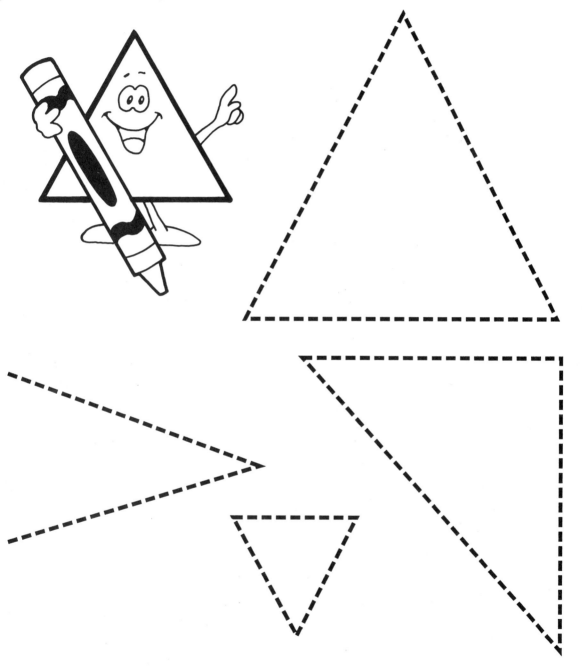

Small, Medium, and Large Triangles

Match by size. Color.

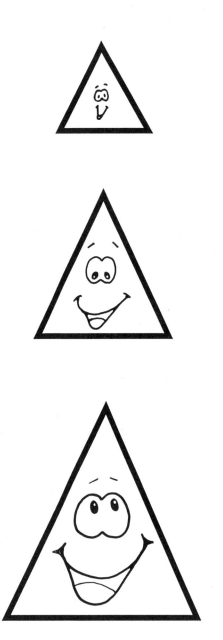

Which Are Triangles?

Color the triangles.

Find the Triangles

Color only the triangles.

I Can Draw Triangles!

Trace.   Draw.

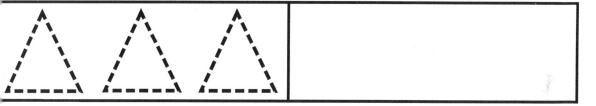

Draw a picture with triangles in it.

Rectangle

Color.

Trace.

rectangle

Let's Make Rectangles

Trace. Color.

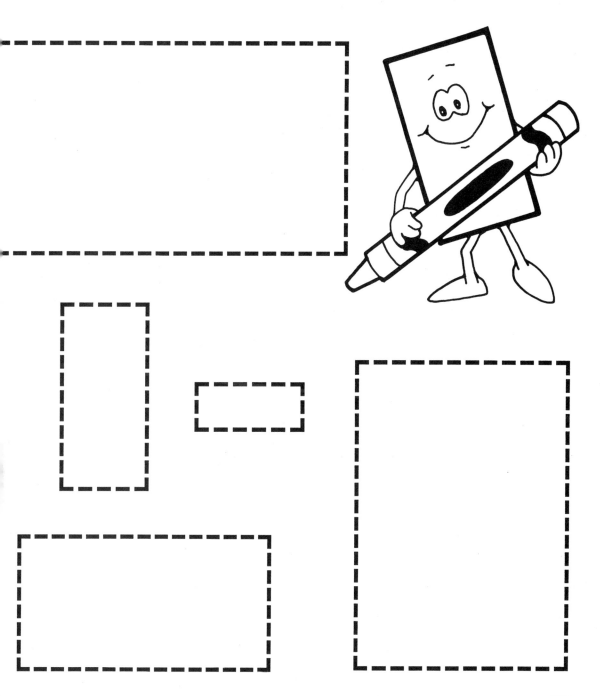

Small, Medium, and Large Rectangles

Match by size. Color.

Which Are Rectangles?

Color the rectangles.

Find the Rectangles

Color only the rectangles.

I Can Draw Rectangles!

Trace.   Draw.

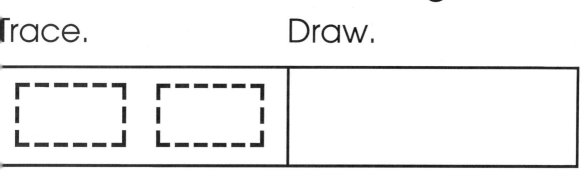

Draw a picture with rectangles in it.

Oval

Color.

Trace.

oval

Let's Make Ovals

Trace. Color.

Small, Medium, and Large Ovals

Match by size. Color.

Brighter Vision Homework Helpe

Which Are Ovals?

Color the ovals.

Find the Ovals

Color only the ovals.

I Can Draw Ovals!

Trace.   Draw.

Draw a picture with ovals in it.

Diamond

Color.

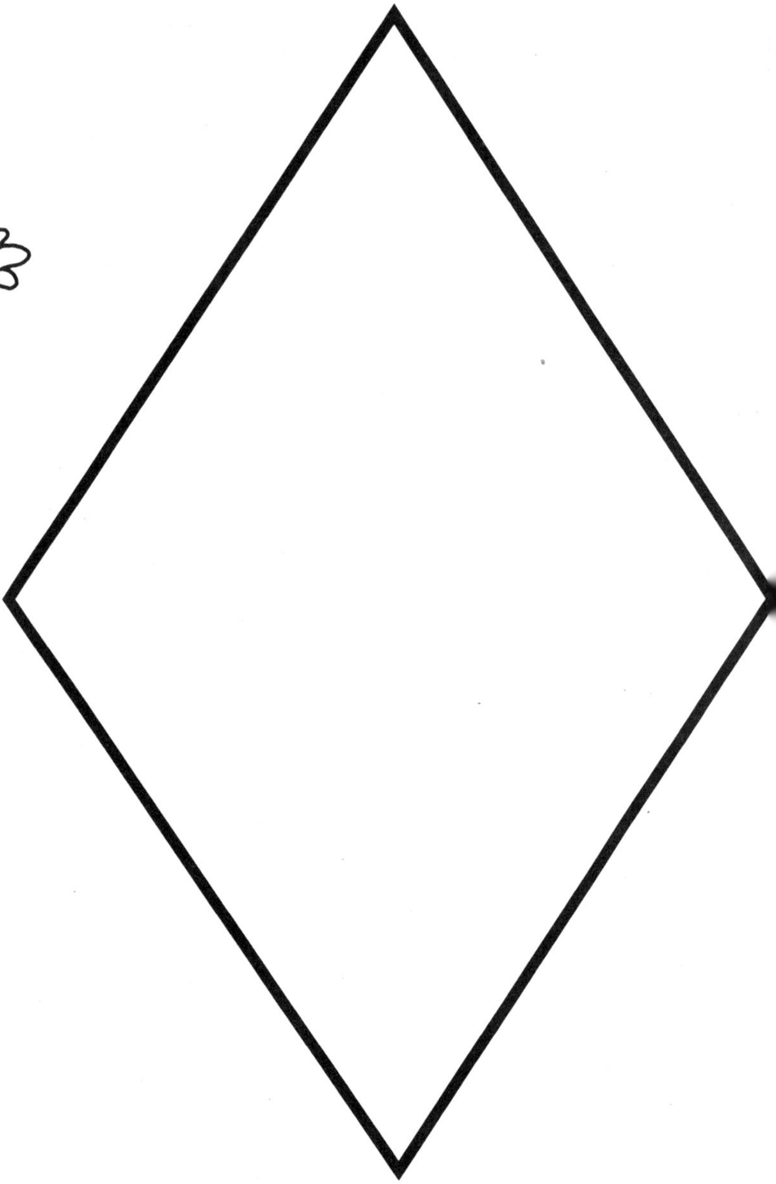

Trace.

diamond

Let's Make Diamonds

Trace. Color.

Small, Medium, and Large Diamonds

Match by size. Color.

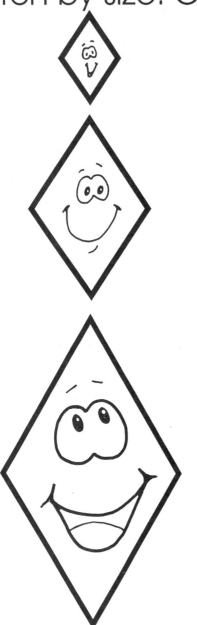
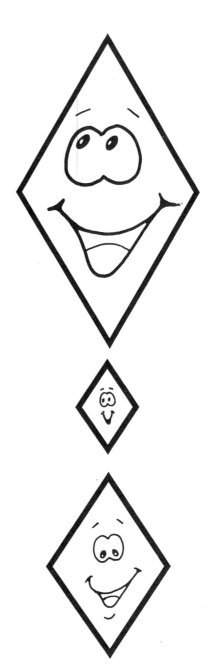

Which Are Diamonds?

Color the diamonds.

Find the Diamonds

Color only the diamonds.

I Can Draw Diamonds!

Trace.   Draw.

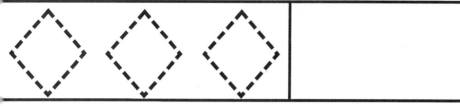

Draw a picture with diamonds in it.

Heart

Color.

Trace.

heart

Let's Make Hearts

Trace. Color.

Small, Medium, and Large Hearts

Match by size. Color.

Which Are Hearts?

Color the hearts.

Find the Hearts

Color only the hearts.

I Can Draw Hearts!

Trace.   Draw.

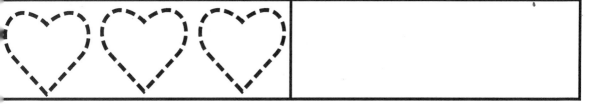

Draw a picture with hearts in it.

Star

Color.

Trace.

star

Let's Make Stars

Trace. Color.

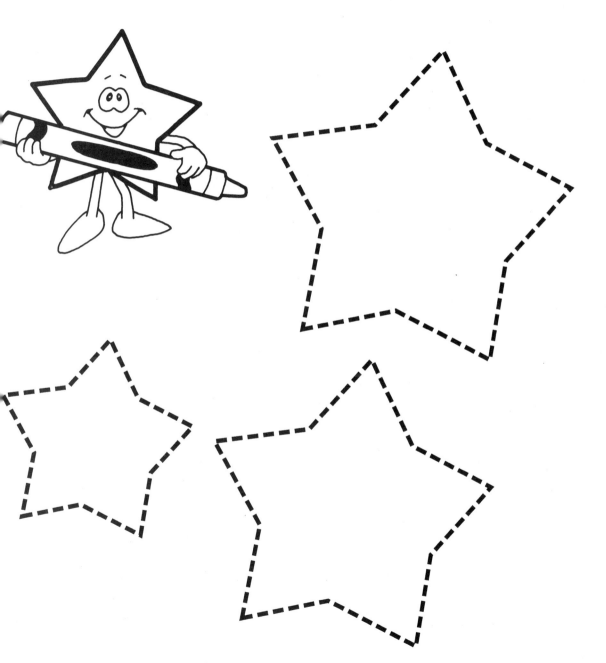

Small, Medium, and Large Stars

Match by size. Color.

198

Which Are Stars?

Color the stars.

Find the Stars

Color only the stars.

I Can Draw Stars!

Trace.   Draw.

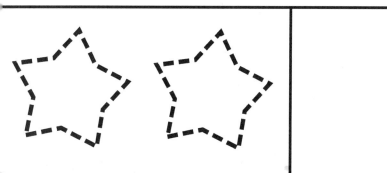

Draw a picture with stars in it.

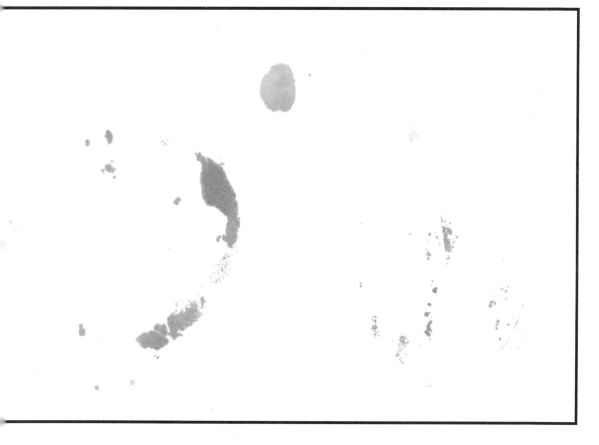

Everyday Shapes

Match. Color.

Shapes All Around Us

Match. Color.

The Color Red

Color the pictures red.

red

Brighter Vision Homework Helper

Red Things

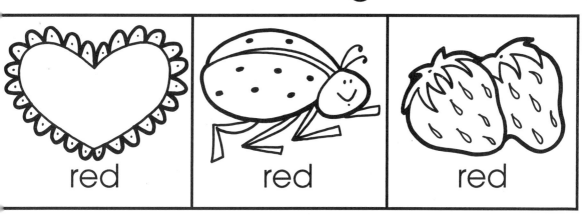

| red | red | red |

Draw a picture of something that is red.

Red and Not Red

Color.

An apple is red.

A wagon is red.

An elephant is not red.

Brighter Vision Homework Helper

Things That Are Red

Color the things that are red.

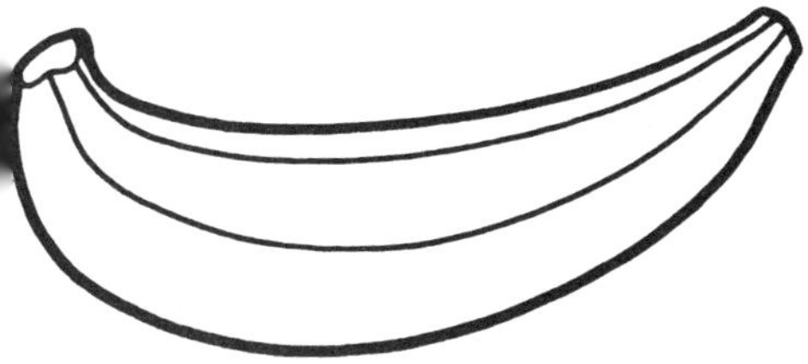

banana

tomato

lamb

apple

cherries

The Way Out

Color the red things to get out of the maze.

The Color Blue

Color the pictures blue.

blue

Blue Things

| blue | blue | blue |

Draw a picture of something that is blue.

Blue and Not Blue

Color.

A blue jay is blue.

A blueberry is blue.

A banana is not blue.

Things That Are Blue

Color the things that are blue.

bear

blue jay

jeans

leaf

blueberries

A Blue Mystery Picture

Color spaces with ♥ blue.
Color spaces with ★ yellow.

The Color Yellow

Color the pictures yellow.

yellow

Yellow Things

| yellow | yellow | yellow |

Draw a picture of something that is yellow.

Yellow and Not Yellow

Color.

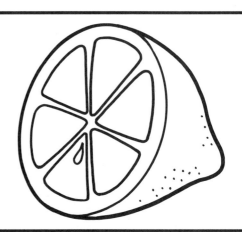

A lemon is yellow.

A chick is yellow.

A sea lion is not yellow.

Things That Are Yellow

Color the things that are yellow.

stop sign

sun

jeans

duck

corn

Red, Blue, and Yellow

In each row, color things that are the same color.

The Color Green

Color the pictures green.

green

Green Things

| green | green | green |

Draw a picture of something that is green.

Green and Not Green

Color.

A leaf is green.

A cucumber is green.

A beaver is not green.

Things That Are Green

Color the things that are green.

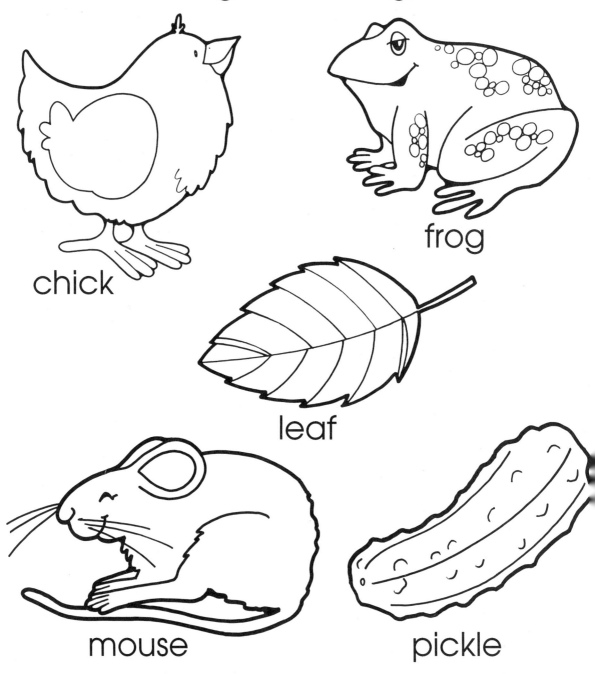

chick

frog

leaf

mouse

pickle

The Way Out

Color the green things to get out of the maze.

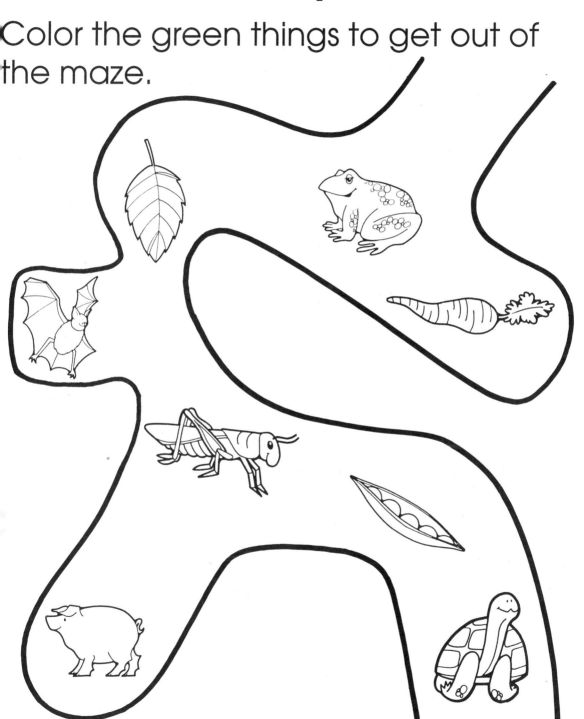

The Color Orange

Color the pictures orange.

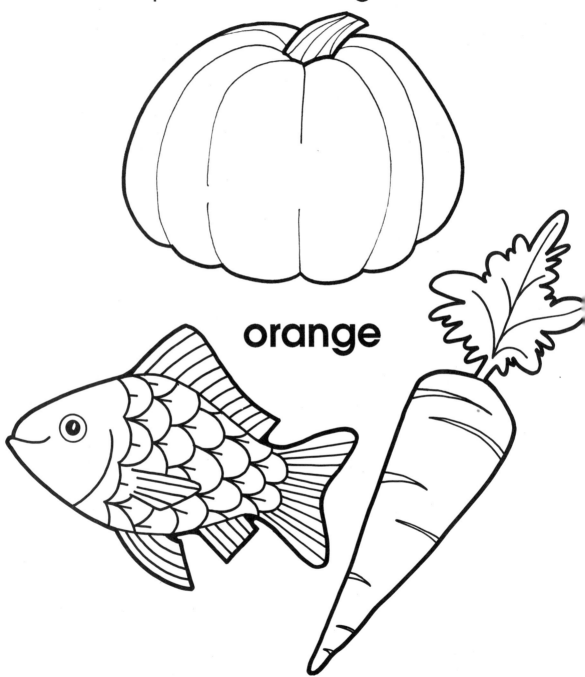

orange

Orange Things

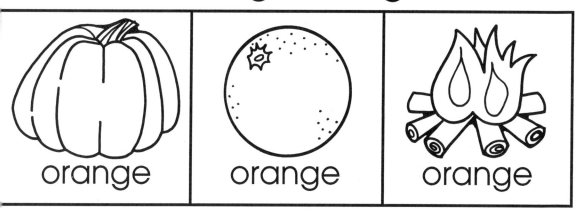

orange   orange   orange

Draw a picture of something that is orange.

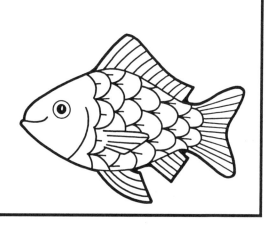

Orange and Not Orange

Color.

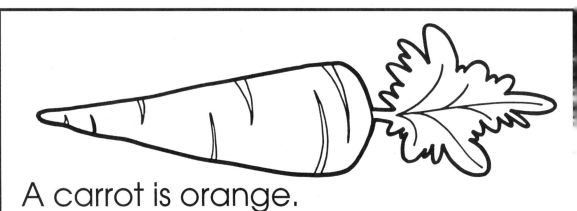

A carrot is orange.

A goldfish is orange.

A lamb is not orange.

Things That Are Orange

Color the things that are orange.

pig

pumpkin

log

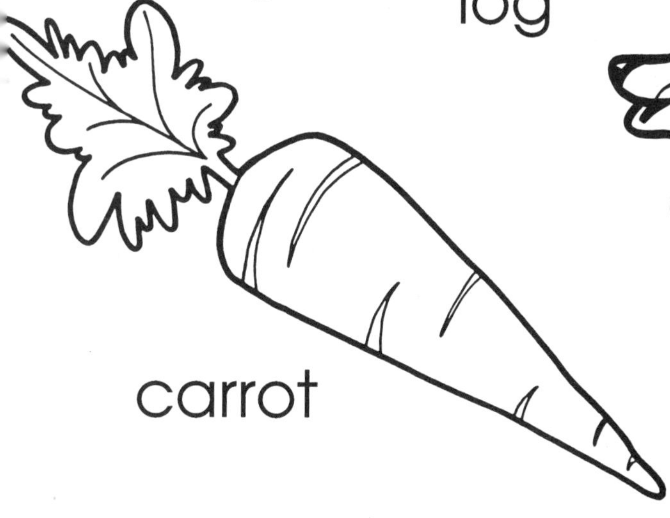

carrot

fox

An Orange Mystery Picture

Color spaces with ■ orange.
Color spaces with ● blue.

The Color Purple

Color the pictures purple.

purple

Purple Things

| purple | purple | purple |

Draw a picture of something that is purple.

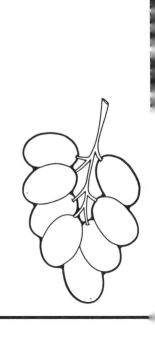

Purple and Not Purple

Color.

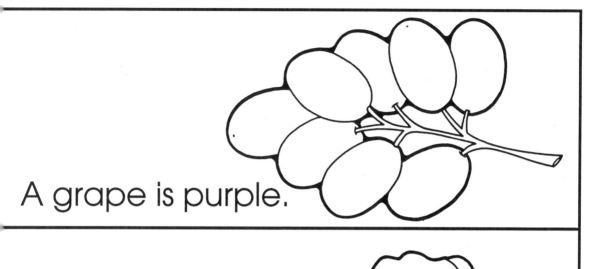

A grape is purple.

A pansy is purple.

A bunny is not purple.

Things That Are Purple

Color the things that are purple.

grapes

pansy

frog

plum

snowflake

Green, Orange, and Purple

n each row, color things that are the same color.

The Color Brown

Color the pictures brown.

brown

Brown Things

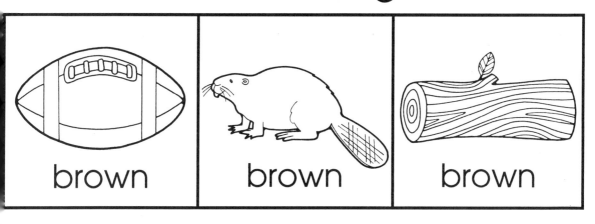

| brown | brown | brown |

Draw a picture of something that is brown.

Brown and Not Brown

Color.

A bear is brown.

A log is brown.

The sun is not brown.

Things That Are Brown

Color the things that are brown.

stop sign

igloo

football

gingerbread

gorilla

The Way Out

Color the brown things to get out of the maze.

Brighter Vision Homework Helper

Black

Color the pictures black.

black

Black Things

black	black	black

Draw a picture of something that is black.

Black and Not Black

Color.

A bat is black.

A sea lion is black.

A lion is not black.

Things That Are Black

Color the things that are black.

top hat

lemon

bat

sea lion

apple

A Black Mystery Picture

Color spaces with × black.
Color spaces with ○ blue.

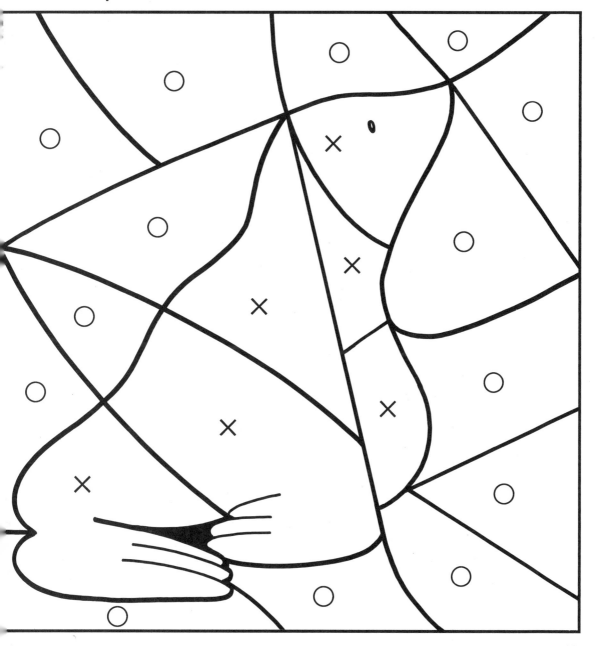

White

Color the pictures white.

white

White Things

white   white   white

Draw a picture of something that is white.

Things That Are White

Color the things that are white.

snowman

bat

igloo

light bulb

snowflake

The Color Pink

Color the pictures pink.

pink

Pink Things

pink   pink   pink

Draw a picture of something that is pink.

Things That Are Pink

Color the things that are pink.

pig

leaf

rose

sun

flamingo

The Color Gray

Color the pictures gray.

gray

Brighter Vision Homework Helper

Gray Things

gray   gray   gray

Draw a picture of something that is gray.

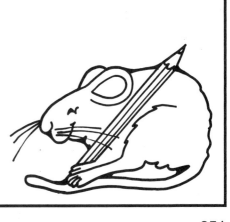

Things That Are Gray

Color the things that are gray.

donkey

apple

mouse

banana

elephant

White, Pink, and Gray

In each row, color things that are the same color.

Many Colors

Color each picture the correct color.

Sailing Fun

Color: ◢ blue   ☆ purple   ☐ black

♡ red   ⬭ brown   ○ yellow

▭ green   ◇ orange

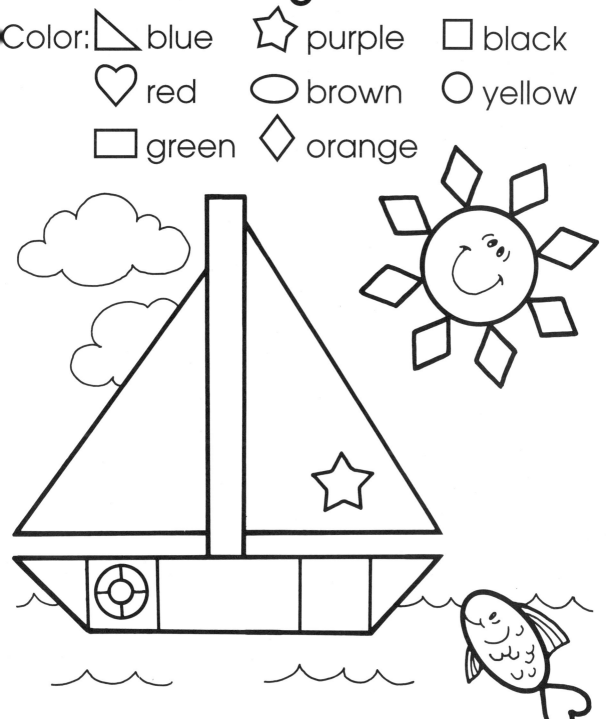

Old Mother Goose

Old Mother Goose,
When she wanted to wander,
Would ride through the air
On a very fine gander.

Where Is Mother Goose?

Follow the maze with your pencil.

Jack Be Nimble

Jack be nimble,
Jack be quick,
Jack jump over
The candlestick.

Brighter Vision Homework Helpe

Let's Compare

Color the largest picture in each row.

Little Miss Muffet

Little Miss Muffet
Sat on a tuffet,
Eating her curds and whey.

Along came a spider,
Who sat down beside her,
And frightened Miss Muffet away.

Spiders

Draw a spider in the box below.

1   2   3

One, Two, Buckle My Shoe

One, two, buckle my shoe.
Three, four, shut the door.
Five, six, pick up sticks.
Seven, eight, lay them straight.
Nine, ten, a big fat hen.

Count and Color

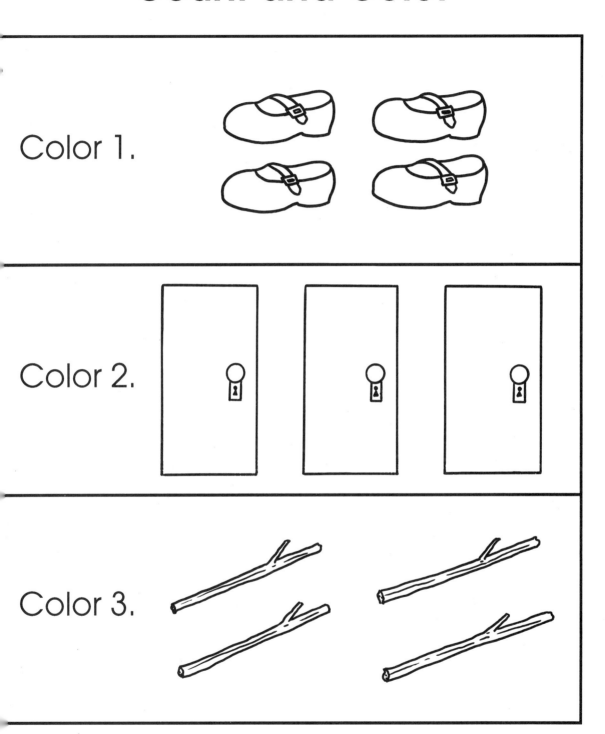

Color 1.

Color 2.

Color 3.

Little Jack Horner

Little Jack Horner sat in a corner
Eating a Christmas pie.
He put in his thumb,
And pulled out a plum,
And said, "What a good boy am I!"

Time to Draw

Draw the missing parts.

Hickory, Dickory, Dock

Hickory, dickory, dock,
The mouse ran up the clock.
The clock struck one,
Down he did run.
Hickory, dickory, dock.

BONG

Alike or Different?

Color two in each row that are alike.

Little Bo-Peep

Little Bo-Peep has lost her sheep,
And can't tell where to find them.
Leave them alone,
And they'll come home,
Wagging their tails behind them.

Find the Sheep

Follow the maze with your pencil.

There Was an Old Woman

There was an old woman
Lived under a hill,
And if she's not gone,
She lives there still.

Look Carefully!

Draw the missing parts.

Hey, Diddle, Diddle

Hey, diddle, diddle,
The cat and the fiddle,
The cow jumped
Over the moon.

The little dog laughed
To see such sport,
And the dish ran away
With the spoon.

Over the Moon

Trace and color.

Fuzzy Wuzzy

Fuzzy Wuzzy was a bear.
Fuzzy Wuzzy had no hair.
Fuzzy Wuzzy wasn't fuzzy,
Was he?

Teddy Bear Time

Draw a bear in the box below.

1   2   3

Little Boy Blue

Little Boy Blue, come blow your horn!
The sheep's in the meadow,
The cow's in the corn.

Where is the boy
Who looks after the sheep?
He's under the haystack, fast asleep.

Time for a Nap

Trace and color.

Polly, Put the Kettle On

Polly, put the kettle on,
Polly, put the kettle on,
Polly, put the kettle on,
And let's have tea.

HOME
SWEET
HOME

Tea Time

Color the largest picture in each row.

Old Mother Hubbard

Old Mother Hubbard
Went to the cupboard,
To get her poor dog a bone.
But when she got there,
The cupboard was bare,
And so the poor dog had none.

Something for Rover

Connect the dots from one to ten.
Color the picture.

Star Light, Star Bright

Star light, star bright,
First star I see tonight,
I wish I may, I wish I might
Have the wish I wish tonight.

Make a Wish!

Connect the dots from 1 to 10.
Color the picture.

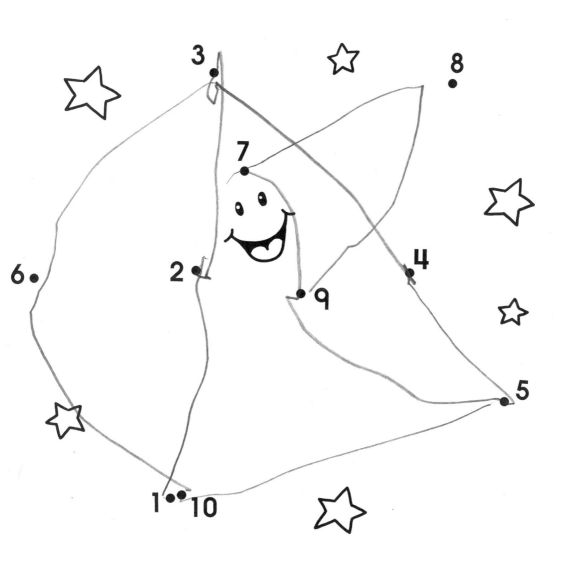

Baa, Baa, Black Sheep

Baa, baa, black sheep,
Have you any wool?
Yes, sir, yes, sir,
Three bags full.
One for my master,
One for my dame,
And one for the little boy
Who lives down the lane.

Count and Color

Color 2.

Color 3.

Color 1.

Pussy Cat, Pussy Cat

Pussy cat, pussy cat,
Where have you been?
I've been to London
To look at the queen.
Pussy cat, pussy cat,
What did you there?
I frightened a little mouse
Under her chair.

286

More Mice

Find six mice hidden in the picture.
Color the picture.

Diddle, Diddle Dumpling

Diddle, diddle dumpling,
My son John,
Went to bed with his stockings on.

One shoe off and one shoe on,
Diddle, diddle dumpling,
My son John.

Alike or Different?

Draw lines between the matching shoes.

The Old Woman Who Lived in a Shoe

There was an old woman
Who lived in a shoe.
She had so many children
She didn't know what to do.

She gave them some broth
Without any bread,
She kissed them all gently
And put them to bed.

Trace and Color

Trace along the dotted lines and color the picture.

Humpty Dumpty

Humpty Dumpty sat on a wall.
Humpty Dumpty had a great fall.
All the king's horses
And all the king's men
Couldn't put Humpty Dumpty
Together again.

Humpty Dumpty's Friends

Draw in the missing parts.

Mistress Mary

Mistress Mary, quite contrary,
How does your garden grow?
With cockle shells and silver bells,
And pretty maids all in a row.

Fancy Flowers

Color two that are alike in each row.

Old King Cole

Old King Cole was a merry old soul,
And a merry old soul was he.
He called for his pipe,
And he called for his bowl,
And he called for his fiddlers three.

Where's the Crown?

Connect the dots from one to ten.

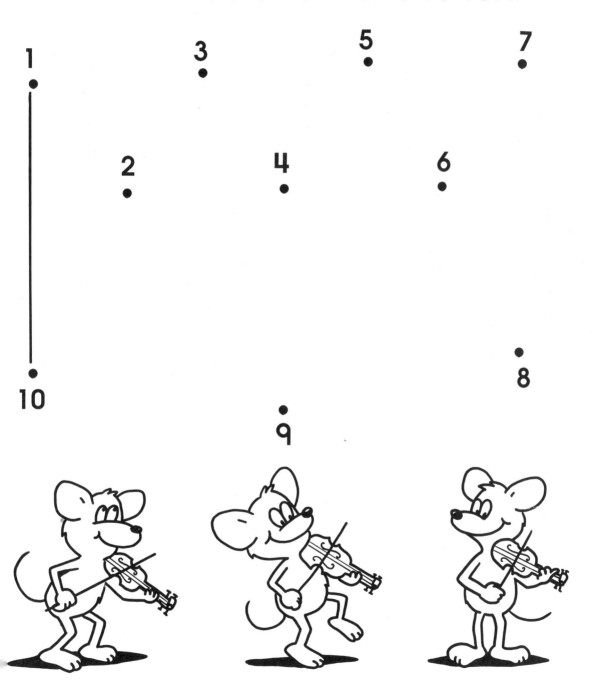

Jack and Jill

Jack and Jill went up the hill
To fetch a pail of water.
Jack fell down,
And broke his crown,
And Jill came tumbling after.

Fetch a Pail of Water

Follow the maze to find the water.

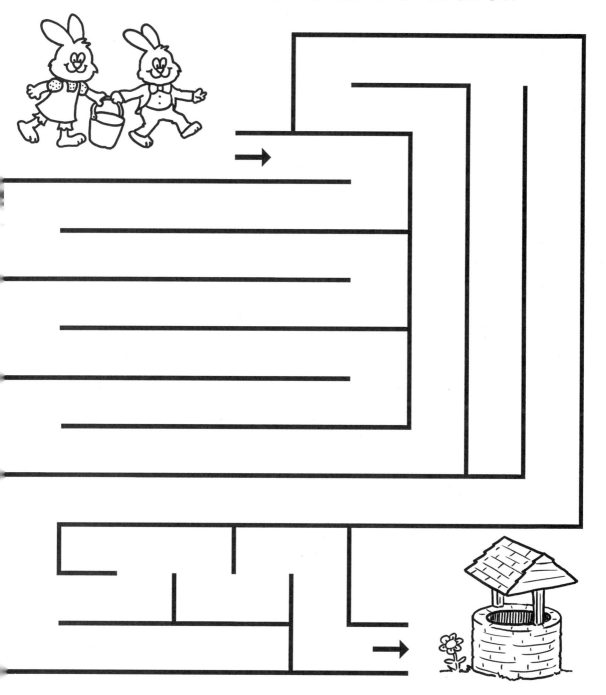

Mary Had a Little Lamb

Mary had a little lamb.
Its fleece was white as snow.
And everywhere that Mary went,
The lamb was sure to go.

It followed her to school one day,
Which was against the rule.
It made the children laugh and play
To see a lamb in school.

Brighter Vision Homework Helpe

Little Lambs

Draw lines between the matching lambs.

To Market

To market, to market,
To buy a fat pig.
Home again, home again,
Jiggety-jig!

Pinky the Pig

Draw a pig in the box below.

1   2   3

Wee Willie Winkie

Wee Willie Winkie
Runs through the town,
Upstairs and downstairs
In his nightgown,
Rapping at the window,
Crying at the lock,
"Are all the children in their beds?
For now it's eight o'clock!"

It's time
for bed!

Matching

Draw lines between the matching pictures.

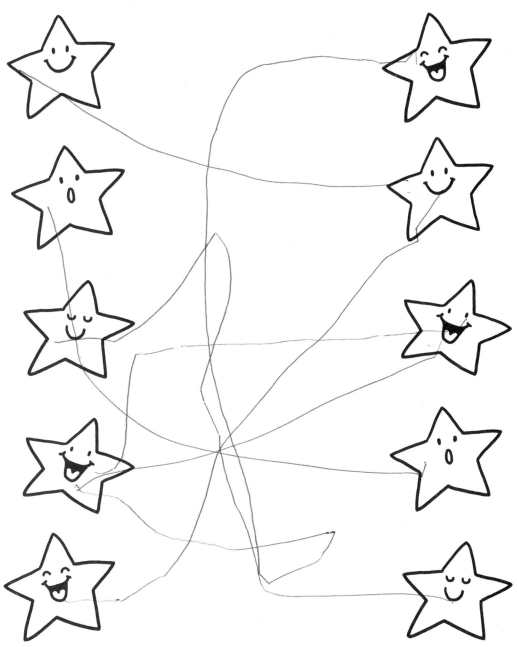

Lion

This lion has a mane.

lion

Elephant

An elephant has a trunk.

elephant

Zebra

A zebra has stripes.

zebra

Camel

This camel has one hump.

camel

Rhinoceros

This rhinoceros has two horns.

rhinoceros

Brighter Vision Homework Helper

Snow Leopard

A snow leopard has spots.

snow leopard

Tiger

A tiger has stripes.

tiger

Panda

A panda has black and white fur.

panda

Kangaroo

A kangaroo has a pouch for its baby.

kangaroo

Anteater

An anteater has a long snout.

anteater

Monkey

A monkey has long arms and legs.

monkey

Brighter Vision Homework Helpe

Bear

A bear has long curved claws.

bear

Whale

This whale has long flippers.

317

whale

Alligator

An alligator has sharp teeth.

alligator

Python

A python has a strong body.

319

python